W0200141

Kingston upon Hull City Libraries
WITHDRAWN
FROM STOCK
SALE

Planet Breetheezy!

by Peter Fardell
edited by Alison Hedger

A new musical about the disadvantages of smoking, to support anti-smoking topics and campaigns.

THE EASIEST WAY TO STOP SMOKING IS NEVER TO START!

A fun musical with a serious message for all young people
Suitable for Primary Schools, especially Juniors
Could also suit some Lower Secondary children

Approximate duration 45 minutes
CD included with Sound Effects

SONGS

1. Smoky Old World	*Foulairians and Choir*
2. Give Him All Your Money	*Foulairians and Choir*
3. The Ocean of Space	*Four Foulairian friends and Choir*
4. Funky Welcome	*Breetheezians and Choir*
5. What Do They Do For You?	*Four friends, Breetheezians and Choir*
6. Never Lose Sight Of Your Dreams	*Gasper and Choir (could involve whole cast)*
7. Party In Paradise	*All cast and Choir*

TEACHER'S BOOK
complete with production notes and music

The script is in the separate PUPIL'S BOOK GA11253

The accompanying CD allows schools to learn the songs quickly and is most useful for rehearsals. The tracks without vocals are intended for use in a performance.

A licence should be obtained from Music Sales Limited for performances of this work.

© Copyright 2001 Golden Apple Productions
A division of Chester Music Limited
8/9 Frith Street, London W1V 3JB

Teacher's Book & CD Order No. GA11231

CAST

THE FOULAIRIANS

Dirty, sad and very untrendy characters who cough a lot. Non-speaking, dancing optional extras can be included at the start of the show in Song 1, 'SMOKY OLD WORLD', and in Song 2, 'GIVE HIM ALL YOUR MONEY'.

There are five speaking parts for the Foulairians

Four Foulairian friends, who need to be strong singers:

Yellowfingers	Could be male or female. To some extent is the Foulairian leader and is the last character to stop smoking. He/she has the worst yellow-stained fingers and skin. Solo singing in Song 5, 'WHAT DO THEY DO FOR YOU?'
Smellbad	A girl smoker who is particularly miserable and grumpy. She smells even worse than the other Foulairians! Solo singing in Song 5, 'WHAT DO THEY DO FOR YOU?'
Stonybroke	A boy who is always hard up, due to spending all his money on cigarettes. Solo singing in Song 5, 'WHAT DO THEY DO FOR YOU?'
Gasper	A boy, and the most likable Foulairian. He has the worst breathing problems, and has the most to gain by leaving the smoky environment. He is by far the most positive of the four friends. Solo singing in Song 5, 'WHAT DO THEY DO FOR YOU?' and in Song 6, 'NEVER LOSE SIGHT OF YOUR DREAMS'.
Mister Ash	A nasty money-grabbing person, who sells expensive cigarettes to anyone. Sings one solo line in the chorus of Song 2, 'GIVE HIM ALL YOUR MONEY'.

THE BREETHEEZIANS

Far more attractive characters that the Foulairians. They are trendy, interesting, sporty, healthy and cool. Non-speaking extra Breetheezians can be involved in singing and dancing in Song 4, 'FUNKY WELCOME' and Song 7, 'PARTY IN PARADISE'.

There are four speaking parts for the Breetheezians.

Dancer	An energetic, lively girl who loves to dance.
Boots	An incredible boy footballer. He is not conceited about his talent and welcomes anyone onto his team.
Dude	He says very little. His main characteristic is that he looks up-to-the-minute and fantastically cool!

Knowalot	Either a boy or girl. A very clever, pleasant person who is always willing to help.
A Choir (*optional*)	Other children not involved as Foulairians or Breetheezians.

COSTUMES AND MAKE UP

The Foulairians and Breetheezians are not exactly human, but neither are they alien life forms. Children should be able to identify with the characters, although perhaps a few features such as antennae could be fun.

The main thing to consider in the costumes and make up, is how to make the Foulairians look unhealthy, grimy and pathetic. They are dirty-looking and have yellow-stained fingers.
Mister Ash could wear a grimy shop coat.

The Breetheezians should look super-fit, fashionable, laid back and cool. These characters wear whatever is "in" at the time of production.

PROPS

- The only props which potentially cause problems are, of course, the cigarettes. It is suggested that you make these as unrealistic as possible, using over-sized tubes, so they are easily seen. They could be brightly coloured or black, to differentiate them from real cigarettes, looking unappealing and ridiculous. The cigarettes need to convey the idea of smoking without being attractive.

- Bundles of old drab clothes

- Boxes marked: chocolate bars
  crisps
  microwave food
  baked beans
  computer games

- Four suitcases

- Barrow, bearing Mister Ash's logo: MISTER ASH - CIGS TO DIE FOR!
  The barrow is overflowing with a huge load of "cigarettes" (*see above*).

- A football

- A sign reading: ONE WEEK LATER for Scene 4

- One real cigarette packet (*empty of cigarettes, but with one imitation cigarette inside*)

SCENES AND SETS

There a four scenes and three sets:

Scene 1 **Planet Foulair**

Scene 2 **Inside Gasper's Spaceship**

Scene 3 **Planet Breetheezy**

Scene 4 **Planet Breetheezy One Week Later**

Set 1 Planet Foulair
A drab, dirty, smoky, miserable backdrop. If resources are limited, use one drab, dirty curtain.

Set 2 Inside Gasper's Spaceship
A recognisably home-built spaceship, suitable for inter-galactic flight!
Lots of dials, knobs and levers. A sign hangs on the wall: NO SMOKING.

Set 3 Planet Breetheezy
A colourful, vibrant, beautiful and exciting backdrop, with green and colourful plants, clear blue sky and exciting clean-cut buildings. A bright, multi-coloured curtain would suffice if resources are limited.

INFORMATION ABOUT THE SONGS

Song 1 **SMOKY OLD WORLD**

A song to establish the opening scene. It can be sung by all Foulairians and the choir, if used. Actions/dance make the song into a visually exciting entertainment. You could use a separate body of dancing Foulairians, perhaps taking these children from the choir.

Song 2 **GIVE HIM ALL YOUR MONEY**

This song is sung by the Foulairians and the choir, if used. Mister Ash has a solo for one line. As the song progresses, Mister Ash sells his "cigarettes" one by one, to various customers, claiming his money to fit in with the lyrics.

Song 3 **THE OCEAN OF SPACE**

A poignant song as the spaceship cruises through space. It is led by Yellowfingers, Smellbad, Stonybroke and Gasper. The choir, if used, sing too. Lighting effects if possible, add an extra dimension to the song.

Song 4 **FUNKY WELCOME**

A rhythmic, finger-snapping, toe-tapping number, sung by the Breetheezians (and choir) welcoming the Foulairians to their planet. If possible, a slick dance routine should feature with this song.

Song 5 WHAT DO THEY DO FOR YOU?
A question and response song. The Breetheezians pose the questions, with solo responses from Yellowfingers, Smellbad, Stonybroke and Gasper. As the song progresses, the Foulairians become less confident and grow doubtful. They gradually come to realise what the lyrics mean.

Song 6 NEVER LOSE SIGHT OF YOUR DREAMS
This is an anthem with a message, sung in the first instance, as a solo by Gasper. Others (a few, or everyone) and/or the whole choir can join in the second time, as preferred.

Song 7 PARTY IN PARADISE
A happy, all-singing, all-dancing, show-stopping finale. All the cast and choir are involved. Some verses can be allocated as solos if preferred.

THE ACCOMPANYING CD

The music required for rehearsals and performances is included on the CD. Each song has two separate tracks; one with vocals and one without. Also included are weird, wonderful and humourous mechanical noises for an abortive take-off, a successful launch of the spaceship, and a safe landing.

SMOKING – SOME FACTS

Tobacco arrived, from the New World, about five hundred years ago and has been inhaled here ever since. However, cigarette smoking as a mass habit only took off in the 20th century. Unfortunately by the time the appalling health risks were realised, smoking was already very fashionable and the appeal of cigarettes has never completely gone away.

Cigarettes are the greatest single cause of avoidable illness and early death in Britain, yet every day about 450 children start smoking. Most adult smokers would like to stop, but almost all of them started when they were still of school age.

In the U.K. it is illegal to sell cigarettes to anyone under 16, but nearly a quarter of this country's 15 year olds smoke regularly, and it has been estimated that those in the 11–15 age bracket smoked over a thousand million cigarettes in one year (1994) alone! These cigarettes cost around £135 million.

Smoking can cause lung cancer, heart disease, bronchitis, emphysema and other illnesses. Less serious, but extremely unattractive side-effects include poor skin condition, stained fingers and teeth, and a nasty stale odour which lingers on the breath, hair and clothes. Passive smoking means that anyone near a smoker also suffers the risks and effects, particularly if they are one of Britain's 3.5 million asthmatics. Every year at least 17,000 young children are admitted to hospital as a result of their parents' smoking habit.

There are many, many more facts and figures to discourage people from smoking; far too many to mention here. Remember: *The easiest way to stop smoking is never to start!*

54072007284445

ONE SMOKY OLD WORLD

Opening Number

Foulairians and Choir

With syncopated resignation! ♩ = 120

KINGSTON UPON HULL
CITY LIBRARIES

Am D7 G C7 G C7
sick - ly.
- nec - tion?
Smo - ky old world,
cho - ky old world,
G C7 G G C7
smo - ky old, cho - ky old world.
We buy cig - ar - ettes to
Ev - ery-thing's grey, what
1.
G C7 A7 D9 G D7
try to for - get we're liv - ing in a smo - ky old world.
more can we say? We're

2.
A7 D9 G E7
liv - ing in a smo - ky old world. We're
A7 D9 G E7
cry - ing in a smo - ky old world. We're
A7 D9 G
dy - ing in a smo - ky old world. *Cough, Cough!*
mp

TWO GIVE HIM ALL YOUR MONEY

Foulairians and Choir

Cue: Ah! Here come my ciggies. Thank you Mister Ash!

To finish
F
Give it all to Mis - ter Ash!
to continue
F Bb F
1. Are there things you want to buy? Do you
2. — You want to buy some sweets, so you
3. You can spend it on ice cream or sup -
Bb F Bb F
real - ly, real - ly try to save up all your mon - ey in a
set off down the street. You've got five pounds and for - ty - sev - en
- port your fav - ourite team, or buy a new com - pu - ter game to -

C7 F D7
tin? You could be a mill - ion - aire, spend - ing
p. So you should still have e - nough to
- day. A brand new moun - tain bike or
Gm B♭m6 F C7 F
mon - ey ev - ery-where, un - less you'd ra - ther give it all to him!
get some oth - er stuff, Mr Ash: un - less you'd ra - ther give it all to me!
an - y - thing you like, un - less you'd ra - ther give it all a - way!

THREE THE OCEAN OF SPACE

Yellowfingers, Smellbad, Stonybroke, Gasper and Choir

Cue: Wow! (cough, cough) I wonder where we're going to?

2.
Link
C F C7 F
race.
Four Friends: We can't tell what we'll
E7 F E7
find when we get where we are go - - ing.
F Dm G7
So we'll just wait and see then, since we've got no way of know - ing!

C Am Dm G7
Four Friends and Choir: 3. Cruis - ing through the black void, ev - ery - where is night.
mp
C A7 Dm G7 C Am
Look out, there's an ast - eroid or a me - teo - rite! This is where you'll find us,
Dm G7 C F C Cmaj7
sail - ing through the O - cean of Space.

FOUR FUNKY WELCOME

Breetheezians

Cue: Hang on . . . someone's coming!

1.
G7♭9
C
G7
Chill out with us an - y - way.
sit back and en - joy the view.
2.
C
F7
3. We don't in - tend to ask you, "What's your
C
F7
game here?"
Makes no dif - ference,

G7
we're still ve - ry glad you came here. _
C G C
4. May - be you need a rest? _ What - ev - er suits you best. _
G
_ Step through our o - pen door. _

G7♭9
There's no-thing that we'd like, there's no-thing that we'd like,
there's no-thing that we'd like more!
C
C7 F6 Dm7/9 Bdim7/G C C7 F♯dim7 Fm6 C C7
tremolo

FIVE WHAT DO THEY DO FOR YOU?

Stonybroke, Gasper, Smellbad, Yellowfingers, Breetheezians and Choir

Cue: What do these cig . . . cigarettes do for you anyway?

D G D A7
eyes are sore when I've had a cig - ar - ette. But I still buy more, when I've
smell so strong when I've had a cig - ar - ette. It's a ghast - ly pong, when I've
D G D
had a cig - ar - ette. So I'm ve - ry poor when I've had a cig - ar - ette.
had a cig - ar - ette. And it stays so long when I've had a cig - ar - ette.
Chorus
A7 D A7
That's what they do for me!
Breetheezians & Choir:
What do they do for you?

What do they do for you? What do they do for you?
What do they do for you?
Gasper: 2. I'm a wheez - y bloke when I've
Yellowfingers: 5. Well, my skin's all stained when I've
D
G D A7
had a cig - ar - ette. 'Cos I breathe the smoke when I've had a cig - ar - ette. And it
had a cig - ar - ette. And my breath - ing's pained when I've had a cig - ar - ette. And my

D G D A7
makes me choke when I've had a cig - ar - ette.
life is drained when I've had a cig - ar - ette.
That's what they do for
D G D
me!
Breetheezians: 3. That's the choice you made, it's
Breetheezians: 6. We're not ones to shout, we
A7 D G
your choice an - y - way. Or were you just a -
won't com - plain or moan. You must have thought it

D
E7
A7
- fraid of what your friends would say?
out, or don't you have a mind of your own? (to Final Chorus)
Final Chorus
A7
Breetheezians & Choir: What do they do for you? What do they do for you?
What do they do for you? What do they do for you?
D
D6

SIX NEVER LOSE SIGHT OF YOUR DREAMS

Gasper and Choir (could involve whole cast)

Cue: If you must.

C E7 F Fm
True friends be - long and they won't for - sake you,
D7 G7 C C7
no mat - ter how it all seems. Re - mem - ber
F Fm C
riv - ers go right to the o - cean, but

Am D7 G7
they on - ly start out as streams. So
C E7 F Fm
try to be strong, then no - thing can break you, and
D7 G7 C A D7
nev - er lose sight of your dreams, nev - er lose
to repeat
to finish
G7 C G7 C
sight of your dreams.
Choir plus any/all cast: You've
f

SEVEN PARTY IN PARADISE

All cast and Choir

(apportion lyrics to individuals or groups as appropriate)

Cue: Well, don't repair that! Let's party!

Chorus
G C7 F6 B♭
par - ty in pa - ra - dise!
Let's have the
F B♭ F
great-est par - ty there has ev - er been.
B♭ F G7 C
(x3)
Let's par - ty in a way this plan - et's nev-er seen!

D G7 C7
4. There's loads of food and drink, just help your-self to ice.
D G C7
It's time at last I think to par-ty in pa-ra-dise!
F D7 G C7 F D7
Par-ty in pa-ra-dise!
G7add9 C7 F F6
cresc. al fine
Par-ty in pa-ra-dise! (shouted) Yeah!
cresc. al fine
ff

New from Golden Apple this year!

Wormzzz! Takes the classroom down to a grass roots level, to look at nature from a more wriggly perspective! Containing seven brilliant new songs and dances by Douglas Wootton, this lively musical teaches children about the vital role worms play in nature.
Wormzzz! is ideal for topic work and can be used to support other areas of the curriculum.
Order No. GA11130

Double Trouble, written by Peter Fardell, uses catchy tunes and clever lyrics to teach mathematical concepts. Ideal for whole-class lessons where knowledge and skills are introduced, developed or reinforced. All the songs are valuable for leading on to questioning and problem-solving activities.
Order No. GA11143

Allygaloo! is a collection of nine brilliant new ideas for Primary school music lessons, written by Alison Hedger, one of Britain's best known composers for children. Fun songs, poems and much more...
Order No. GA11176

Robin's Christmas Sing-along!
Robin's passion is to sing. He happily joins in with all the Christmas music, but this doesn't make him very popular. The stars redeem the situation, and take him to the Bethlehem stable, where he leads a Christmas sing-along with all the animals and characters from the play.
A charming story with clever songs that implement the National Curriculum for Music Requirements.
Written by Niki Davies.
Order No. GA11220